Fiona Mapp

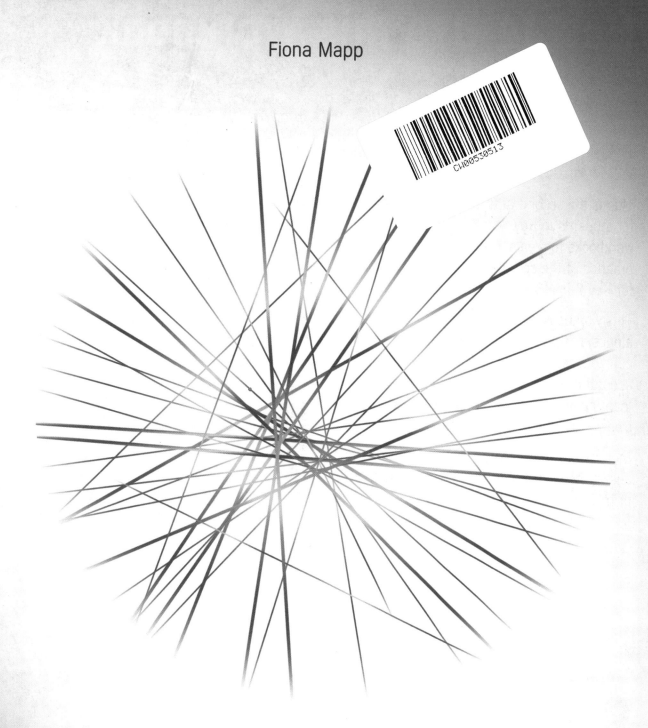

ESSENTIALS

Year 8
KS3 Mathematics
Workbook

How to Use this Workbook

A Note to the Teacher

This is the second of three maths workbooks for students in Key Stage 3. Together, the workbooks for Years 7, 8 and 9 provide practice of the complete programme of study for Key Stage 3 Maths.

This workbook has been written to be used alongside the Key Stage 3 Maths Year 8 coursebook. The questions are grouped according to level, to support personalised learning and to enable students to track their own progress.

Included in the centre of the book is a pull-out answer booklet. It contains the answers to all of the questions in this workbook.

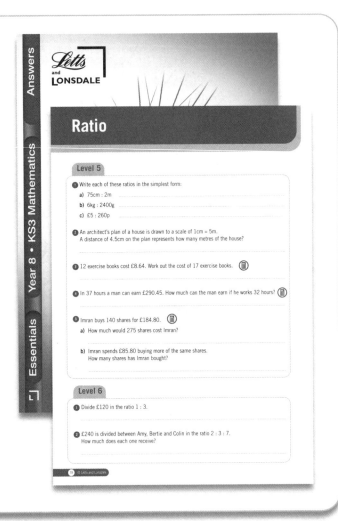

A Note to the Student

We're sure you'll enjoy using this workbook, but follow these helpful hints to make the most of it:

- Try to write answers that require reasoning or explanation in good English, using correct punctuation and good sentence construction. Read what you have written to make sure it makes sense.
- Think carefully when drawing graphs. Always make sure you have accurately labelled your axes, given your graph a title and plotted points accurately.

- Where questions require you to make calculations, remember to show your workings. In tests, you might get marks for a correct method even if you arrive at the wrong answer.
- The tick boxes on the Contents page let you track your progress: simply put a tick in the box next to each topic when you're confident that you know it.

You might need a calculator to answer questions that carry this symbol. All other questions should be attempted without using a calculator and you should show your workings.

Contents

4 Numbers ☐

8 Fractions, Decimals and Estimating ☐

12 Negative Numbers ☐

14 Percentages ☐

18 Ratio ☐

20 Number Patterns and Sequences ☐

22 Working with Algebra ☐

26 Equations and Inequalities ☐

30 Graphs ☐

36 Shapes and Measures ☐

38 Angles ☐

40 Transformations ☐

44 Perimeter, Area and Volume ☐

48 Handling Data ☐

52 Averages ☐

54 Probability ☐

IBC Acknowledgements

Numbers

1 Work out…

a) 256 x 32

d) 698 x 87

b) 379 x 65

e) 729 x 49

c) 506 x 73

f) 397 x 56

2 Work out…

a) 52 $\overline{)884}$

c) 15 $\overline{)435}$

b) 14 $\overline{)322}$

d) 51 $\overline{)816}$

3 A train carriage can hold 123 people. If a train has 13 carriages, how many people can it transport?

4 Bottles of lemonade cost 67p each. Tammy buys 28 bottles for a party. How much does Tammy spend?

5 Hewi is holding a conference. He needs 3200 biscuits. One packet holds 37 biscuits.

a) How many packets must he buy?

b) How many spare biscuits will he have?

c) Each packet of biscuits costs 82p. How much will Hewi spend on biscuits?

6 Jackie works in an office. She has 28 reams of paper. Each ream has 180 sheets of paper.

a) How many sheets of paper does Jackie have?

b) Jackie is making a booklet. Each booklet has 43 sheets of paper.
How many complete booklets can Jackie make?

7 Write the following with index notation, e.g. $4 \times 4 \times 4 = 4^3$

a) $5 \times 5 \times 5 \times 5$

c) $9 \times 9 \times 9 \times 9 \times 9 \times 9 \times 9$

b) $7 \times 7 \times 7 \times 7 \times 7$

d) $8 \times 8 \times 3 \times 3 \times 3 \times 3$

8 Work out…

a) $5 + 6 \times 2$

d) $(7 + 3)^2 - 9$

b) $9 - (3 \times 2)$

e) $20 \times (5 + 1)^2 - 9$

c) $(7^2 + 3^2) - (2 \times 5)$

f) $9^2 \div 4 - 2 \times 3$

9 Next to each problem is a set of numbers. You may use only the numbers provided. No number can be used twice. Use these numbers to fill in the boxes to make the numbers at the end.

Example, (1, 2, 3, 4, 5) $\boxed{3}$ + $\boxed{2}$ x $\boxed{4}$ = 11

a) (1, 2, 3, 4, 5) $\boxed{}$ ÷ $\boxed{}$ + $\boxed{}$ = 3

b) (1, 2, 3, 4, 5) $\boxed{}$ x $\boxed{}$ + $\boxed{}$ x $\boxed{}$ = 22

c) (2, 3, 4, 5, 6) $\boxed{}$ – $\boxed{}$ x $\boxed{}$ + $\boxed{}$ = 5

d) (2, 3, 4, 5, 6) $\boxed{}$ x $\boxed{}$ – $\boxed{}$ x $\boxed{}$ = 22

10 From this list of numbers, 27, 32, 2, 5, 7, 13, 16, 25, 24, 1, 8, write down…

a) the factors of 16 ....

c) the cube numbers ....

b) the square numbers ....

d) the prime numbers ....

Level 6

1 Work out…

a) 7^2 ....

c) 4^3 ....

b) $\sqrt{64}$ ....

d) $\sqrt[3]{1000}$ ....

2 Complete the prime factor tree to work out the prime factors of 180.

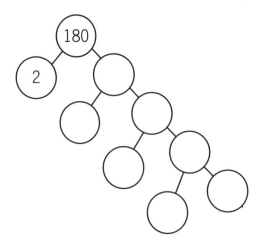

Prime factors of 180 = ...

3 Work out the prime factors of:

a) 25 ....

c) 48 ....

....

b) 60 ....

d) 56 ....

....

4 a) i) Express 72 and 96 as a product of their prime factors.

72 = ...

96 = ...

ii) Use your answers to 4. a) i) to work out the highest common factor (HCF) of 72 and 96.

....

iii) Use your answers to 4. a) i) to work out the lowest common multiple (LCM) of 72 and 96.

....

5 a) Find the HCF of 24 and 36. ....

b) Write 120 as a product of its prime factors. ....

....

6 Find the LCM of 42 and 70. ....

6 Using a calculator, work out the following, writing down all the digits on your calculator display:

a) $\dfrac{7.3^2 + 2.6^3}{11.2 - 1.4}$ ....

c) $\dfrac{\sqrt{15.4 - 7.6}}{3.25 + 8.3}$ ....

b) $\dfrac{(6.9^4) \times 3}{\sqrt{12.4}}$ ....

d) $\dfrac{\sqrt{9.2^3 + 1.5}}{3.7 \times 2.1}$ ....

Fractions, Decimals & Estimating

1 Work out...

a) $\frac{1}{3}$ of 840kg _____

b) $\frac{2}{7}$ of £21 _____

c) $\frac{9}{11}$ of £99 _____

d) $\frac{4}{7}$ of 28cm _____

e) $\frac{3}{5}$ of 45kg _____

f) $\frac{7}{9}$ of 27ml _____

2 Eileen buys a sofa for £650. She pays a deposit of $\frac{1}{5}$ of the purchase price. How much was Eileen's deposit?

_____

_____

3 Work out...

a) 27.5 x 2.4 _____

b) 18.6 x 3.9 _____

c) 27.5 x 4.5 _____

d) 11.57 ÷ 1.3 _____

e) 48.16 ÷ 2.8 _____

f) 48.05 ÷ 3.1 _____

4 Jonathan did this calculation: 42.5 x 6.1 = 259.25
Write down a calculation that he could do to check that he is correct.

_____

_____

1 Work out...

a) $\frac{7}{9} + \frac{1}{3}$ ....

b) $\frac{6}{11} + \frac{2}{33}$ ....

c) $\frac{2}{3} + \frac{3}{5}$ ....

d) $\frac{7}{12} + \frac{5}{7}$ ....

e) $\frac{7}{9} - \frac{2}{3}$ ....

f) $\frac{9}{10} - \frac{3}{7}$ ....

2 Work out...

a) $\frac{2}{7} \times \frac{1}{3}$ ....

b) $\frac{6}{11} \times \frac{2}{3}$ ....

c) $\frac{5}{9} \times \frac{1}{2}$

d) $\frac{12}{17} \div \frac{2}{3}$ ....

e) $\frac{7}{12} \div 1\frac{1}{6}$ ....

f) $\frac{9}{14} \div 1\frac{1}{2}$ ....

3 Work out...

a) $2\frac{1}{3} + 4\frac{1}{7}$ ....

b) $6\frac{1}{4} - 3\frac{2}{5}$ ....

c) $5\frac{1}{3} \times 2\frac{4}{7}$ ....

d) $7\frac{3}{5} \div \frac{3}{5}$ ....

4 A plank of wood is $4\frac{2}{3}$ m long. $1\frac{5}{8}$ is sawn off. What length of the plank is left?

....

....

5 There are $3\frac{1}{2}$ litres of milk in a bowl. $\frac{6}{7}$ of a litre of milk is added to the bowl. How much milk is now in the bowl?

....

....

6 Place the following decimals in order of size, smallest first.

a) 6.3, 5.7, 4.9, 4.08, 6.31, 6.02

b) 17.3, 14.6, 17.21, 14.73, 17.209, 14.72

c) 9.6, 9.42, 9.48, 9.53, 9.05, 9.12

d) 14.1, 15.9, 16.7, 16.32, 15.19, 14.12

7 During the men's decathlon in the Olympics, the following distances (in metres) were thrown for the discus.

45.27, 47.71, 53.79, 50.04, 45.80, 50.91, 45.50, 45.39.

Place these distances in order of size, smallest first.

8 Round these numbers to 1 decimal place:

a) 12.72   e) 14.55

b) 16.97   f) 37.69

c) 21.07   g) 51.75

d) 28.63   h) 29.38

9 Round these numbers to 2 decimal places:

a) 7.639   e) 15.625

b) 14.255   d) 12.529

c) 37.639   g) 572.735

d) 12.529   h) 8921.073

1 Round the following to the number of significant figures, shown in brackets.

a) 5635 (3s.f.) ....

b) 2.0394 (3s.f.) ....

c) 117.3025 (4s.f.) ....

d) 2569 (2s.f.) ....

e) 193 (2s.f.) ....

f) 5.0723 (4s.f.) ....

g) 1254 (2s.f.) ....

h) 29657 (1s.f.) ....

2 Estimate the answers to the following by rounding them to 1 significant figure.

a) 607 x 49 ....

b) 37 x 913 ....

c) 49 x 0.62 ....

d) 796 x 47.2 ....

e) $(7.9)^2$ ....

f) $\dfrac{29 \times 31}{10.6}$ ....

g) $\dfrac{79 \times 9.3}{0.41}$ ....

3 Work out...

a) 7500 x 0.01 ....

b) 274 x 0.02 ....

c) 333 ÷ 0.01 ....

d) 592 ÷ 0.02 ....

e) 750 ÷ 0.0005 ....

f) 639 ÷ 0.003 ....

Negative Numbers

1 Work out...

a) 7 + -2 ....

b) 6 – -3 ....

c) -7 + -2 ....

d) -9 – -4 ....

e) 6 – + 9 ....

f) 15 – -3 ....

g) -12 + -6 ....

h) -10 – -5 ....

i) -37 + -15 ....

j) 18 – -6 ....

2 The temperature is -3°C. If the temperature rises by 9°C, what is the new temperature?

....

3 The temperature in Oslo at midday is -2°C. In London, the temperature at midday is 6°C. What is the difference in temperature at midday between Oslo and London?

....

4 Katie has £69 in her bank account. She writes a cheque for £113. After the cheque has been cashed, what will Katie's bank balance show?

....

5 In a magic square, the rows, columns and diagonals all add up to the same number. This is the magic number. Complete the following magic squares to find their magic numbers.

a)

2	-5	3
	5	

Magic number =

b)

		-1
-2	7	1

Magic number =

c)

		-2
	-1	
0		2

Magic number =

Level 6

1 Work out…

a) 5 x -3 _____

b) -6 x -2 _____

c) -4 x 9 _____

d) -9 x 3 _____

e) -8 x 7 _____

f) -7 x -7 _____

g) -6 x -4 _____

h) 12 x -4 _____

i) -6 x -3 _____

j) 9 x -8 _____

k) -8 x 3 _____

l) -7 x -2 _____

m) $(-6)^2$ _____

n) $(-5)^2$ _____

2 Work out…

a) $12 \div (-4)$ _____

b) $(-60) \div 5$ _____

c) $(-36) \div 9$ _____

d) $20 \div (-2)$ _____

e) $(-30) \div (3)$ _____

f) $(-55) \div 11$ _____

g) $(-21) \div (-3)$ _____

h) $(-9) \div (-3)$ _____

i) $16 \div (-4)$ _____

j) $(-24) \div 2$ _____

k) $56 \div (-7)$ _____

l) $\sqrt[3]{-8}$ _____

3 Use your calculator to answer the following:

a) $[-7 + (-2)] \times (-5)$ _____

b) $((-6)^2 + 4) \times (-2)$ _____

c) $(-3 \times -5) + (-6)$ _____

d) $-9 - [(-4) \times 2]$ _____

e) $(-6)^2 + (-3 \times -4)$ _____

f) $\sqrt{9} - (4 \times -2)$ _____

4 Look at the list of numbers: 4, -3, 5, -2

Choose numbers from the list to make each statement correct.

a) 5 x ☐ = -15

b) 7 – ☐ = 9

c) -24 ÷ ☐ = -6

d) $(-3)^2$ x ☐ = 45

Percentages

1 In a garden centre the price of garden furniture is reduced by 30% at the end of summer. Find the sale price of each of the following:

a) Garden Table was £400

b) Lawnmower was £120

c) Sunlounger was £84

2 VAT at 15% is added to the items below. Calculate the price of each item including VAT.

a) Hedge Trimmer was £62

b) Dining Table was £280

c) Strimmer was £85

3 A salesperson earns £24 500 per year. She is offered a pay rise of 3.8%. How much will she now earn?

4 The number of pupils in a school falls by 7%. If there were originally 840 pupils, how many are there now?

Level 6

1 Write 28cm as a percentage of 4m.

2 Write 95kg as a percentage of 372kg.

3 Simon scores 69 out of 125 in a science test.
What percentage did he get?

4 In a school vote, Sarah got 63 votes, Thomas got 71 votes and Harriet got 59 votes.
What percentage of the votes did Thomas get?

5 Place the following in order of size, smallest first:

a) $\frac{2}{5}$, 0.37, 41%, 0.379, 0.415

b) $\frac{1}{3}$, 30%, 0.32, $\frac{3}{8}$, $\frac{2}{7}$

c) 75%, 0.69, $\frac{8}{9}$, $\frac{2}{13}$, 0.9, 93%

Level 7

1 Last year there were 820 pupils in a school year group. This year there are 920 pupils.
What is the percentage increase in the number of pupils in a school year group?

2 A car originally cost £9200. It now costs £8575. By what percentage has the car been
reduced?

3 A house was bought for £285 000. After three years it was sold for £362 000. 🖩
What is the percentage profit?

_____

_____

_____

4 A shopkeeper bought some tins of ham for 69p each. He sold each tin for 77p. 🖩
What is the percentage profit per tin?

_____

_____

_____

5 A motorbike was bought for £11 500. Two years later it was sold for £9100. 🖩
What is the percentage loss?

_____

_____

_____

6 A jumper cost £32. Six months later it was sold for £24. 🖩
What is the percentage loss?

_____

_____

_____

7 A car was bought for £10 500. During each following year it depreciates by 10%. How much is the car worth after...

a) 1 year?

_____

_____

b) 2 years?

_____

_____

_____

8 A house was bought for £200 000. During each year it increases in value by 15%. How much is the house worth after...

a) 1 year?

_____

_____

b) 2 years?

_____

_____

c) 3 years?

_____

_____

_____

Ratio

1 Write each of these ratios in the simplest form:

   a) 75cm : 2m

   b) 6kg : 2400g

   c) £5 : 260p

2 An architect's plan of a house is drawn to a scale of 1cm = 5m.
A distance of 4.5cm on the plan represents how many metres of the house?

3 12 exercise books cost £8.64. Work out the cost of 17 exercise books.

4 In 37 hours a man can earn £290.45. How much can the man earn if he works 32 hours?

5 Imran buys 140 shares for £184.80.

   a) How much would 275 shares cost Imran?

   b) Imran spends £85.80 buying more of the same shares.
How many shares has Imran bought?

Level 6

1 Divide £120 in the ratio 1 : 3.

2 £240 is divided between Amy, Bertie and Colin in the ratio 2 : 3 : 7.
How much does each one receive?

3 The sides of a triangle are in the ratio 2 : 3 : 4. The perimeter is 72cm.
Find the length of each side.

4 Mr Fruit has an orchard of pear trees and apple trees. The trees are planted in the ratio 4 : 7.
He has 77 trees. How many are pear trees?

5 Some of the ingredients to make 8 biscuits are:

| 400g flour |
| 240g sugar |
| 150g margarine |

How much of each ingredient is needed to make:

a) 12 biscuits?

b) 30 biscuits?

6 At a bank Audrey exchanges £75 for 510 Dirhams.

a) How many Dirhams will she get for £130 at this rate?

b) How much is 5340 Dirhams worth in Pounds Sterling?

7 Which of the following is better value for money?

a) 2kg of sugar at 78p or 1.7kg of sugar at 64p.

b) 50ml of toothpaste at £1.35 or 35ml of toothpaste at 97p.

8 10 builders build a wall in 8 days. How long would it take 4 builders working at the same rate?

Number Patterns and Sequences

1 This pattern sequence is made of grey and white tiles.

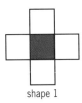

shape 1

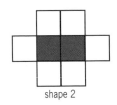

shape 2

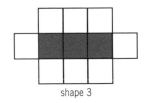

shape 3

a) Draw the next shape in the sequence.

b) Complete the table:

Number of Grey Tiles	1	2	3	4	5
Number of White Tiles	4	6			

c) How many white tiles are there in shape 23?

d) If there are 64 white tiles, how many grey tiles are there?

e) Write down a formula that connects the number of grey tiles and the number of white tiles.

1 For each of the sequences in the tables below, write down:

a)

Position in Sequence	1	2	3	4	5	6
Term	7	10	13	16	19	22

  i) term to term rule ....

  ii) *nth* term ....

b)

Position in Sequence	1	2	3	4	5	6
Term	3	7	11	15	19	21

  i) term to term rule ....

  ii) *nth* term ....

c)

Position in Sequence	1	2	3	4	5	6
Term	5	10	15	20	25	30

  i) term to term rule ....

  ii) *nth* term ....

d)

Position in Sequence	1	2	3	4	5	6
Term	-1	1	3	5	7	9

  i) term to term rule ....

  ii) *nth* term ....

2 Write down the nth term for each of these sequences:

  a) 4, 9, 14, 19, 24,... ....

  b) 5, 7, 9, 11, 13,... ....

  c) 9, 17, 25, 33, 41,... ....

  d) 2, 7, 12, 17, 19,... ....

  e) 7, 6, 5, 4, 3, 2,... ....

  f) 8, 6, 4, 2, 0, -2,... ....

Working with Algebra

1. Simplify these expressions by collecting like terms:

   a) $5a + 3b - 2a + b$ _____

   b) $4n + 3y + 6n - y$ _____

   c) $7b - 2c + 3c + b$ _____

   d) $6t + 5p - p + 7t$ _____

   e) $3x - 4y + 2y - x$ _____

   f) $a^2 + 3b^2 - a^2 + 2b^2$ _____

2. Simplify...

   a) $3x \times 4$ _____

   b) $5m \times 3$ _____

   c) $7a \times 3b$ _____

   d) $2a \times 5x$ _____

   e) $3g \times 7h$ _____

   f) $6a \times a$ _____

   g) $5a \times 2a$ _____

   h) $3x \times 2x^2$ _____

   i) $7y \times 3y^2 \times 2y$ _____

   j) $9m^2 \times 4m \times 3m$ _____

3. In an examination William got y marks.

   a) Adam got eight more marks than William. Write down an expression for the number of marks that Adam got.

   _____

   b) Hannah got 5 times as many marks as William. Write down an expression for the number of marks that Hannah got.

   _____

   c) Rupel got half the marks that Hannah got. Write down an expression for the number of marks that Rupel got.

   _____

4 Daisy and Lily are playing snap with these algebra cards. Daisy shows Lily which pairs of cards are the same.

a) Write down which cards pair up.

| $m \div 4$ | $m4$ | $4 + m$ | m^2 | $\frac{m}{4}$ |

| $3m - 2m$ | $m + 4$ | m | $4m$ | $m \times m$ |

....

....

....

....

....

b) Lily decides to write four more cards. For each card below, write out another card that could be its pair.

i) $7m - 3m$ **ii)** m^3 **iii)** $\frac{1}{6}m$

....

5 Multiply out the brackets:

a) $5(a - 3)$ ....

b) $6(a + 2)$ ....

c) $7(a - 3)$ ....

d) $5(2a + 1)$ ....

e) $3(2a - 4)$ ....

f) $6(4 - 2a)$ ....

g) $5(2 - a)$ ....

h) $10(5a + 1)$ ....

i) $3(2a - 4)$ ....

j) $4(5a - 1)$ ....

Level 6

1 Multiply out the brackets:

a) $-3(a + 4)$ _____

b) $-4(a + 3)$ _____

c) $-6(a - 5)$ _____

d) $-2(a - 3)$ _____

e) $-3(2a + 1)$ _____

f) $-4(a - 3)$ _____

g) $-5(2a - 3)$ _____

h) $-(a + 5)$ _____

i) $-(a - 7)$ _____

j) $-(2a - 6b - 3c)$ _____

2 Expand…

a) $5x(2x - 3y)$ _____

b) $2x(3x + y)$ _____

c) $5x(3 - 2x)$ _____

d) $6y(3y - 2x)$ _____

e) $-5y(2y - 3x)$ _____

f) $3x(2x - 4y)$ _____

g) $2x(4x + 2y)$ _____

h) $-3x(8x + 2y)$ _____

i) $-4y(6y - 3x)$ _____

j) $-5(5y + 12x)$ _____

3 Expand and simplify…

a) $3(x + 4) + 2(x + 1)$ _____

b) $5(x + 3) + 2(x + 7)$ _____

c) $6(x - 4) + 3(x - 1)$ _____

d) $9(2x - 1) + 5(x - 2)$ _____

e) $7(3x + 4) - 2(x + 1)$ _____

f) $8(4x - 6) - 3(2x - 1)$ _____

g) $7(5x + 6) - (5x - 3)$ _____

h) $9(3x - 1) - 7(2x - 6)$ _____

Level 6 (cont.)

4 Simplify…

a) $a^6 \times a^4$

b) $m^4 \times m^9$

c) $p^6 \times 2p^7$

d) $3p^4 \times 5p^{10}$

e) $6p^7 \times 3p^9$

f) $7m^6 \times 2m^4$

g) $5m^{10} \times 3m$

h) $9m^6 \times 2m^7$

i) $x^6 \times x^3$

j) $10x^4 \times 5x^5$

5 Factorise…

a) $5x + 10$

b) $6x - 24$

c) $3x + 18$

d) $6x + 20$

e) $15x - 5y$

f) $7y + 14x$

g) $12y - 10x$

h) $3x + 27y$

i) $9x - 3y$

j) $15x + 30y$

6 Factorise…

a) $x^2 + 10x$

b) $x^2 - 6x$

c) $3x^2 + 9x$

d) $6x^2 - 2x$

7 Find the value of the following expressions if $a = 4$, $b = -2$ and $c = -3$

a) $a^2 + b$

b) $2a^2 - c$

c) $3a - 2b$

d) $5c^2 + 2b$

e) $\dfrac{c^2}{2} + 4a$

f) $\dfrac{3b - 4c}{-2}$

8 If $a = \dfrac{2b^2c}{3d}$ find a if $b = 5$, $c = -4$ and $d = -10$.

Equations and Inequalities

1 Solve the following equations:

a) $5x + 1 = 11$

b) $6x - 4 = 8$

c) $3x - 1 = 17$

d) $10x + 5 = 20$

e) $\dfrac{x}{2} + 1 = 6$

f) $5 - 2x = 10$

g) $3 - 4x = 11$

h) $\dfrac{x}{7} - 4 = 2$

2 Solve the following equations:

a) $2x + 7 = x + 10$

b) $5x + 2 = 3x + 8$

c) $4x - 1 = 2x + 9$

d) $7x - 3 = 2x + 12$

e) $10x - 4 = 8x - 6$

f) $6x - 1 = 3x + 14$

g) $12x + 5 = 6x + 17$

h) $8 + 2x = 5x - 4$

3 Solve the following equations:

a) $6(2x + 1) = 12$

e) $3(x + 2) + 2(x + 5) = 36$

b) $7(4x - 4) = 28$

f) $2(2x + 1) + 3(x - 2) = 24$

c) $5(x - 3) = 25$

g) $5(3x + 6) + 2(x + 1) = 49$

d) $4(x + 2) + 2(x + 3) = 26$

h) $6(x + 3) = 2(x - 1)$

4 For each of the following...

    i) write an equation to solve the problem.

    ii) solve the equation to find x.

a) x is a number. Multiply x by 4 and add 3. The answer is 31.

    i)

    ii)

b) x is a number. Multiply x by 5 and subtract it from 20. The answer is 30.

    i)

    ii)

c) x is a number. Multiply x by 3 and add 7. The answer is 22.

    i)

    ii)

5 The perimeter of this rectangle is 60cm. (*Not to scale*)

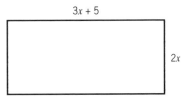

a) Write down the equation for the perimeter.

b) Solve the equation.

c) Write down the length and width of the rectangle.

   i) Length =

   ii) Width =

6 Use the information in this diagram to:

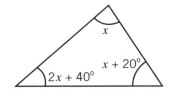

a) Form an equation.

b) Solve the equation to find x.

7 Isabel thinks of a number. She multiplies it by 3 and subtracts 5. Her answer is the same as if she'd multiplied the number by 2 and subtracted 4. What number did Isabel think of?

Letts
and
LONSDALE

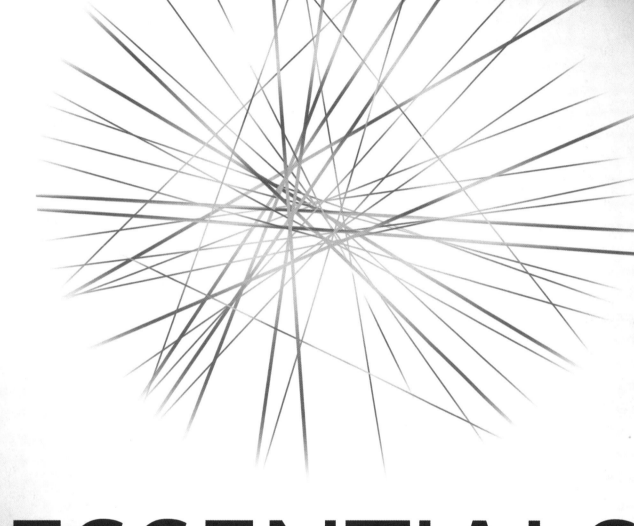

ESSENTIALS

Year 8
KS3 Mathematics
Workbook Answers

NUMBERS

Pages 4–7

Level 5

1. a) 8192

   b) 24 635

   c) 36 938

   d) 60 726

   e) 35 721

   f) 22 232

2. a) 17

   b) 23

   c) 29

   d) 16

3. 1599 people.

4. £18.76

5. a) 87 packets.

   b) 19 biscuits.

   c) £71.34

6. a) 5040 sheets of paper.

   b) 117 booklets.

7. a) 5^4

   b) 7^5

   c) 9^7

   d) $8^2 \times 3^4$

8. a) 17

   b) 3

   c) 48

   d) 91

   e) 711

   f) 3

9. a) $4 \div 2 + 1 = 3$

   b) $5 \times 2 + 3 \times 4 = 22$

   c) $6 - 2 \times 3 + 5 = 5$

   d) $6 \times 5 - 4 \times 2 = 22$

10. a) 2, 16, 1, 8

    b) 25, 16

    c) 27, 8

    d) 2, 5, 7, 13

Level 6

1. a) 49

   b) ±8

   c) 64

   d) 10

2.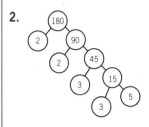

   Prime factors of 180 =
   $2 \times 2 \times 3 \times 3 \times 5 = 2^2 \times 3^2 \times 5$

3. a) $25 = 5 \times 5 = 5^2$

   b) $60 = 2 \times 2 \times 3 \times 5$
      $= 2^2 \times 3 \times 5$

   c) $48 = 2 \times 2 \times 2 \times 2 \times 3$
      $= 2^4 \times 3$

   d) $56 = 2 \times 2 \times 2 \times 7$
      $= 2^3 \times 7$

4. a) i) $72 = 2 \times 2 \times 2 \times 2 \times 3 \times 3 = 2^3 \times 3^2$

      $96 = 2 \times 2 \times 2 \times 2 \times 2 \times 3 = 2^5 \times 3$

   ii) HCF = $2 \times 2 \times 2 \times 3 = 24$

   iii) LCM = $2 \times 2 \times 2 \times 2 \times 2 \times 3 \times 3 = 288$

5. a) HCF = 12

   b) $120 = 2 \times 2 \times 2 \times 3 \times 5$
      $= 2^3 \times 3 \times 5$

6. LCM = 210

Level 7

1. a) 7.23122449

   b) 1931.108943

   c) 0.241805022

   d) 3.587913997

FRACTIONS, DECIMALS AND ESTIMATING

Pages 8–11

Level 5

1. a) 280kg

   b) £6

   c) £81

   d) 16cm

   e) 27kg

   f) 21ml

2. £130

3. a) 66

   b) 72.54

   c) 123.75

   d) 8.9

   e) 17.2

   f) 15.5

4. Either $259.25 \div 42.5$ or $259.25 \div 6.1$

Level 6

1. a) $1\frac{1}{9}$

   b) $\frac{20}{33}$

   c) $1\frac{4}{15}$

   d) $1\frac{25}{84}$

   e) $\frac{1}{9}$

   f) $\frac{33}{70}$

2. a) $\frac{2}{21}$

   b) $\frac{4}{11}$

   c) $\frac{5}{18}$

   d) $1\frac{1}{17}$

   e) $\frac{1}{2}$

   f) $\frac{3}{7}$

3. a) $6\frac{10}{21}$

   b) $2\frac{17}{20}$

   c) $13\frac{5}{7}$

   d) $12\frac{2}{3}$

4. $3\frac{1}{24}$ m

5. $4\frac{5}{14}$ litres

6. a) 4.08, 4.9, 5.7, 6.02, 6.3, 6.31

   b) 14.6, 14.72, 14.73, 17.209, 17.21, 17.3

   c) 9.05, 9.12, 9.42, 9.48, 9.53, 9.6

   d) 14.1, 14.12, 15.19, 15.9, 16.32, 16.7

7. 45.27, 45.39, 45.501, 45.80, 47.71, 50.04, 50.91, 53.79

8. a) 12.7

   b) 17.0

   c) 21.1

   d) 28.6

   e) 14.6

   f) 37.7

   g) 51.8

   h) 29.4

9. a) 7.64

   b) 14.26

   c) 37.64

   d) 12.53

   e) 15.63

   f) 1037.26

   g) 572.74

   h) 8921.07

Level 7

1. a) 5640

   b) 2.04

   c) 117.3

   d) 2600

   e) 190

   f) 5.072

   g) 1300

   h) 30 000

2. a) $600 \times 50 = 30\,000$

   b) $40 \times 900 = 36\,000$

   c) $50 \times 0.6 = 30$

   d) $800 \times 50 = 40\,000$

   e) $8^2 = 64$

   f) $\frac{30 \times 30}{10} = 9$

   g) $\frac{80 \times 9}{0.4} = 1800$

3. a) 75

   b) 5.48

   c) 33 300

   d) 29 600

   e) 1 500 000

   f) 213 000

NEGATIVE NUMBERS

Pages 12–13

Level 5

1. a) 5
   b) 9
   c) -9
   d) -5
   e) -3
   f) 18
   g) -18
   h) -5
   i) -22
   j) 24

2. 6°C

3. 8°C

4. £-44 (overdrawn by £44).

5. a)

2	-5	3
-1	0	-1
-3	5	-2

   Magic number = 0

   b)

3	-3	6
5	2	-1
-2	7	1

   Magic number = 6

   c)

-4	3	-2
1	-1	-3
0	-5	2

   Magic number = -3

Level 6

1. a) -15
   b) 12
   c) -36
   d) -27
   e) -56
   f) 49
   g) -24
   h) -48
   i) 18
   j) -72
   k) -24
   l) 14

m) 36
n) 25

2. a) -3
   b) -12
   c) -4
   d) -10
   e) 10
   f) -5
   g) 7
   h) 3
   i) 4
   j) -12
   k) -8
   l) -2

3. a) 45
   b) -80
   c) 9
   d) -1
   e) 48
   f) 11

4. a) $5 \times \boxed{-3} = -15$
   b) $7 - \boxed{-2} = 9$
   c) $-24 \div \boxed{4} = -6$
   d) $(-3)^2 \times \boxed{5} = 45$

PERCENTAGES

Pages 14–17

Level 5

1. a) £280
   b) £84
   c) £58.80

2. a) £71.30
   b) £322
   c) £97.75

3. £25 431

4. 781 pupils

Level 6

1. 7%

2. 25.5%

3. 55.2%

4. 36.8%

5. a) 0.37, 0.379, $\frac{2}{5}$, 41%, 0.415
   b) $\frac{2}{7}$, 30%, 0.32, $\frac{1}{3}$, $\frac{3}{8}$
   c) $\frac{2}{13}$, 0.69, 75%, $\frac{8}{9}$, 0.9, 93%

Level 7

1. 12.2%

2. 6.79%

3. 27%

4. 11.6%

5. 20.9%

6. 25%

7. a) £9450
   b) £8505

8. a) £230 000
   b) £264 500
   c) £304 175

RATIO

Pages 18–19

Level 5

1. a) 3 : 8
   b) 5 : 2
   c) 25 : 13

2. 22.5 metres

3. £12.24

4. £251.20

5. a) £363
   b) 65 shares

Level 6

1. £30, £90

2. £40, £60, £140

3. 16cm, 24cm, 32cm

4. 28 pear trees

5. a) 600g flour
      360g sugar
      225g margarine
   b) 1500g flour
      900g sugar
      562.5g margarine

6. a) 884 Dirhams

   b) £780

7. a) 1.7kg for 64p
   b) 50ml at £1.35

8. 20 days

NUMBERS PATTERNS AND SEQUENCES

Pages 20–21

Level 5

1. a)
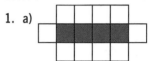

   b)

Number of Grey Tiles	1	2	3	4	5
Number of White Tiles	4	6	8	10	12

   c) 48
   d) 31
   e) $W = 2g + 2$

Level 6

1. a) i) Add 3 each time.
      ii) $3n + 4$
   b) i) Add 4 each time.
      ii) $4n - 1$
   c) i) Add 5 each time.
      ii) $5n$
   d) i) Add 2 each time.
      ii) $2n - 3$

2. a) $5n - 1$
   b) $2n + 3$
   c) $8n + 1$
   d) $5n - 3$
   e) $8 - n$
   f) $10 - 2n$

WORKING WITH ALGEBRA

Pages 22–25

Level 5

1. a) $3a + 4b$
   b) $10n + 2y$
   c) $8b + c$
   d) $13t + 4p$
   e) $2x - 2y$

f) $5b^2$

2. a) $12x$

   b) $15m$

   c) $21ab$

   d) $10ax$

   e) $21gh$

   f) $6a^2$

   g) $10a^2$

   h) $6x^3$

   i) $42y^4$

   j) $108m^4$

3. a) $y + 8$

   b) $5y$

   c) $\frac{5y}{2}$

4. a) $m \div 4, \frac{m}{4}$

   $m4, 4m$

   $m^2, m \times m$

   $3m - 2m, m$

   $4 + m, m + 4$

   b) i) $4m$ or equivalent.

   ii) $m \times m \times m$ or equivalent.

   iii) $m \div 6$ or equivalent.

5. a) $5a - 15$

   b) $6a + 12$

   c) $7a - 21$

   d) $10a + 5$

   e) $6a - 12$

   f) $24 - 12a$

   g) $10 - 5a$

   h) $50a + 10$

   i) $6a - 12$

   j) $20a - 4$

Level 6

1. a) $-3a - 12$

   b) $-4a - 12$

   c) $-6a + 30$

   d) $-2a + 6$

   e) $-6a - 3$

   f) $-4a + 12$

   g) $-10a + 15$

   h) $-a - 5$

i) $-a + 7$

j) $-2a + 6b + 3c$

2. a) $10x^2 - 15xy$

   b) $6x^2 + 2xy$

   c) $15x - 10x^2$

   d) $18y^2 - 12xy$

   e) $-10y^2 + 15xy$

   f) $6x^2 - 12xy$

   g) $8x^2 + 4xy$

   h) $-24x^2 - 6xy$

   i) $-24y^2 + 12xy$

   j) $-25y^2 - 60xy$

3. a) $5x + 14$

   b) $7x + 29$

   c) $9x - 27$

   d) $23x - 19$

   e) $19x + 26$

   f) $26x - 45$

   g) $30x + 45$

   h) $13x + 33$

4. a) a^{10}

   b) m^{13}

   c) $2p^{13}$

   d) $15p^{14}$

   e) $18p^{16}$

   f) $14m^{10}$

   g) $15m^{11}$

   h) $18m^{13}$

   i) x^9

   j) $50x^9$

5. a) $5(x + 2)$

   b) $6(x - 4)$

   c) $3(x + 6)$

   d) $2(3x + 10)$

   e) $5(3x - y)$

   f) $7(y + 2x)$

   g) $2(6y - 5x)$

   h) $3(x + 9y)$

   i) $3(3x - y)$

   j) $15(x + 2y)$

6. a) $x(x + 10)$

b) $x(x - 6)$

c) $3x(x + 3)$

d) $6x(x - 2)$

7. a) 14

   b) 35

   c) 16

   d) 41

   e) $20\frac{1}{2}$

   f) -3

8. $6\frac{2}{3}$

EQUATIONS AND INEQUALITIES

Pages 26–29

Level 6

1. a) $x = 2$

   b) $x = 2$

   c) $x = 6$

   d) $x = 1.5$

   e) $x = 10$

   f) $x = -2.5$

   g) $x = -2$

   h) $x = 42$

2. a) $x = 3$

   b) $x = 3$

   c) $x = 5$

   d) $x = 3$

   e) $x = -1$

   f) $x = 5$

   g) $x = 2$

   h) $x = 4$

3. a) $x = \frac{1}{2}$

   b) $x = 2$

   c) $x = 8$

   d) $x = 2$

   e) $x = 4$

   f) $x = 4$

   g) $x = 1$

   h) $x = -5$

4) a) i) $4x + 3 = 31$

   ii) $x = 7$

b) i) $20 - 5x = 30$

ii) $x = -2$

c) i) $3x + 7 = 22$

   ii) $x = 5$

5. a) $10x + 10 = 60$

   b) $x = 5$

   c) i) Length = 20cm

   ii) Width = 10cm

6) a) $4x + 60° = 180°$

   b) $x = 30°$

7. $3x - 5 = 2x - 4x$

   Isabel's number = 1

8. $x = 1.6$

9. $x = 0.4$

10. a) $6 > 4$

   b) $8 > 7$

   c) $-5 < 4$

   d) $1.6 < 2.8$

   e) $-2 > -7$

   f) $-3 > -6$

11. a)

b)

c)

d)

Activity: 0.45

GRAPHS

Pages 30–35

Level 5

1. a) 7.5 cm

   b) 2.2 inches

2. a) Graph B

   b) Graph D

   c) Graph C

   d) Graph A

Level 6

1. A: $x = 2$

   B: $y = 3$

   C: $y = -1$

D: $y = -x$

E: $x = -3$

F: $y = x$

2. a) $y = x - 5$

x	-3	-1	0	1	3
y	-8	-6	-5	-4	-2

b)

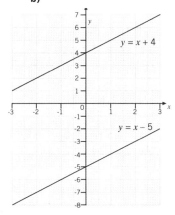

c) $y = x + 4$

x	-3	-1	0	1	3
y	1	3	4	5	7

d) See graph above.

e) They are parallel lines and the constant (number) tells you where the graph cuts the y axis.

3. a) $x + y = 3$

x	-1	0	1	3
y	4	3	2	0

b)

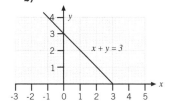

4. a) $y = 2x - 3$

x	-3	0	1	3
y	-9	-3	-1	3

b)

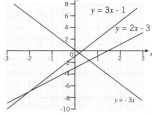

c) $y = 3x - 1$

x	-2	0	1	2
y	-7	-1	2	5

d) See graph above.

e) (-2,-7)

f) See graph above.

g) $y = 3x - 1$

5. a) $y = 2x - 4$: C

b) $y = 2x + 4$: A

c) $y = 4x$: B

6. a) AB: (3,2)

b) CD: (-3,-$\frac{1}{2}$)

c) EF: (1$\frac{1}{2}$,-2)

d) GH: (-$\frac{1}{2}$,1$\frac{1}{2}$)

7. a) $y = x^2 - 4$

x	-3	-2	-1	0	1	2	3
y	5	0	-3	-4	-3	0	5

b)

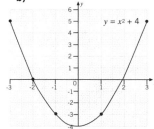

8. a) $y = 2x^2 + 3$

x	-2	-1	0	1	2
y	5	-1	-3	-1	5

b)

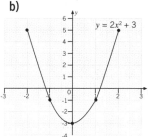

c) (0,-3)

d) $x = 1.2$, $x = -1.2$ (approx.)

9. a) Mrs Hay

b) i) 1200

ii) 30 minutes

c) In the last two hours. Since the graph is steeper he covered 100km in 1$\frac{1}{2}$ hours.

d) Mrs Hay set off from Summerton at 1000, she travelled at a constant speed to Mathstown, where she arrived at 1300. She travelled 200km in 3 hours.

e) The time when Mrs Hay and Mr Davis passed each other.

SHAPES AND MEASURES

Pages 36–37

Level 5

1. a) 15.4lb

b) 50kg

c) 17.5 inches

d) 2.86 litres (2 d.p.)

2. 43.8m

3. 5.75km

4. 70cm

Level 6

1.

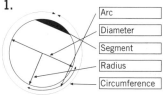

Arc
Diameter
Segment
Radius
Circumference

2. a)   **b)**   **c)**

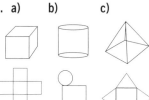

3.

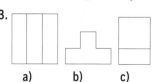

a)   **b)**   **c)**

4.

5. a)

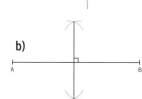

60°

b)

A   B

ANGLES

Pages 38–39

Level 5

1. a) $a = 44°$

b) $a = 105°$

$b = 75°$

c) $a = 131°$

d) $a = 58°$

e) $a = 60°$

f) $a = 54°$

g) $a = 99°$

h) $a = 51°$

$b = 67°$

i) $a = 70°$

$b = 107°$

$c = 77°$

Level 6

1. a) 150°

b) 30°

2. 63°

3. a) $a = 69°$

b) $a = 125°$, $b = 125°$

c) $a = 48°$, $b = 132°$

d) $a = 58°$, $b = 58°$, $c = 122°$

e) $a = 140°$, $b = 140°$

f) $a = 43°$, $b = 137°$, $c = 137°$, $d = 43°$

4. a) i) 060°

ii) 240°

b) i) 125°

ii) 305°

c) i) 210°

ii) 030°

d) i) 110°

ii) 290°

e) i) 320°

ii) 140°

f) i) 115°

ii) 245°

TRANSFORMATIONS

Pages 40–43

Level 6

1. a) – d)

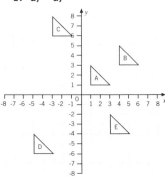

2. a) – e)

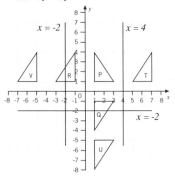

3. a) – b)

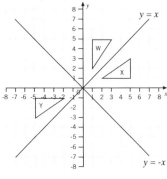

4. a) – d)

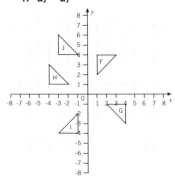

5. a)–b)

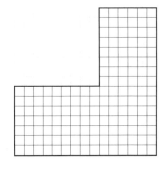

6. a) True

   b) False

   c) True

   d) False

   e) True

7. a) – b)

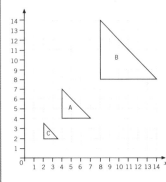

8. a) – b)

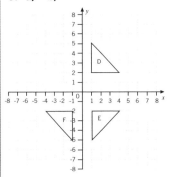

   c) Rotation of 180° about (0,0)

PERIMETER, AREA AND VOLUME

Pages 44–47

Level 5

1. a) i) $25.2cm^2$

      ii) $20.4cm$

   b) i) $135cm^2$

      ii) $47cm$

   c) i) $184.2cm^2$

      ii) $57.4cm$

2. a) 4cm

   b) 7cm

   c) 14cm

3. a) $26.56cm^2$

   b) $66.65cm^2$

   c) $65.4cm^2$

Level 6

1. a) $42cm^2$

   b) $78.2cm^2$

   c) $198cm^2$

2. a) $4.4cm^2$

   b) 9.3cm (1d.p.)

   c) 15.4cm (1d.p.)

3. a) $60cm^2$

   b) $975cm^2$

   c) $160cm^2$

   d) $240cm^2$

   e) $322.5cm^2$

   f) $166.4cm^2$

4. a) $122 cm^2$

   b) $94.5cm^2$

   c) $132.375cm^2$

5. a) i) 50.24cm

      ii) $200.96cm^2$

   b) i) 31.4cm

      ii) $78.5cm^2$

   c) i) 113.04cm

      ii) $1017.36cm^2$

6. a) $981.25cm^2$

   b) $26.41cm^2$

   c) $167.33cm^2$

7. 77.1cm

8. $30.96cm^2$

9. a) i) Volume = $30cm^3$

      ii) SA = $62cm^3$

   b) i) Volume = $1760cm^3$

      ii) SA = $936cm^3$

   c) i) Volume = $756cm^3$

      ii) SA = $552cm^2$

10. 16 crates.

11. a) $530cm^3$

    b) $4050cm^3$

HANDLING DATA

Pages 48–51

Level 6

1. **Example** How many hours of television do you watch per day?

0–1 hr	☐
1 hr 1 min–3 hrs	☐
3 hr 1 min–5 hrs	☐
Over 5 hrs	☐

2. The ages overlap in the tickboxes. For example, which box would a 10-year-old tick? There are two possible boxes.

3. a)

Height (h cm)	Tally	Frequen⋯
$125 \le h < 130$	I	1
$130 \le h < 135$	I	1
$135 \le h < 140$	IIII	4
$140 \le h < 145$	IIII I	6
$145 \le h < 150$	IIII	5
$150 \le h < 155$	IIII	4
$155 \le h < 160$	III	3
$160 \le h < 165$	IIII	4

   b)

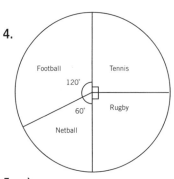

4.

   Football Tennis 120° 60° Rugby Netball

5. a)

	Red	Blue	Green	Tota⋯
Boys	6	12	17	35
Girls	9	7	6	22
Total	15	19	23	57

b) 9

c) 57

6. a)

Unordered

Stem	Leaf
0	6 2 5 2 3 2 1 5
1	5 3 4 3 7 5 4 6 3
2	7 2
3	6

Ordered

Stem	Leaf
0	1 2 2 2 3 5 5 6
1	3 3 3 4 4 5 5 6 7
2	2 7
3	6

Key 1|3 = 13 days

b) 36 days.

7. a)

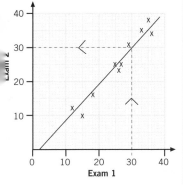

b) See diagram.

c) Approximately 29 marks.

AVERAGES

Pages 52–53

Level 5

1. a) 4.5

b) 4

c) 4

d) 6

2. James. Although Lucy gets a higher mean score, she has a bigger range than James, which indicates that she is not as consistent.

Level 6

1. a) 1.65 goals

b) 2 goals

c) 2 goals

d) 4 goals

2. a) 13.9 years

b) 14 years

c) 14 years

d) 4 years

3. a) i) 22

ii) 22

iii) 35

b) i) 85

ii) 85

iii) 37

c) i) 243.5

ii) 244

iii) 24

d) i) 7.3

ii) 6.8

iii) 3.7

PROBABILITY

Pages 54–55

Level 5

1. a) $\frac{3}{8}$

b) $\frac{1}{8}$

c) $\frac{7}{8}$

d) 0

2. a) $\frac{2}{11}$

b) $\frac{2}{11}$

c) $\frac{4}{11}$

d) $\frac{7}{11}$

Level 6

1. 0.65

2. 72%

3. $\frac{5}{11}$

4. 0.17

5. Gill Keith

C   C

C   O

C   A

O   C

O   O

O   A

A   C

A   O

A   A

C = Cola
A = Apple
O = Orange

6. a)

		Die					
Spinner	+	1	2	3	4	5	6
	1	2	3	4	5	6	7
	3	4	5	6	7	8	9
	4	5	6	7	8	9	10

b) i) $\frac{3}{18} = \frac{1}{6}$

ii) $\frac{3}{18} = \frac{1}{6}$

iii) $\frac{9}{18} = \frac{1}{2}$

iv) $\frac{15}{18} = \frac{5}{6}$

7. a)

Dice 1

x	1	2	3	4	5	6
1	1	2	3	4	5	6
2	2	4	6	8	10	12
3	3	6	9	12	15	18
4	4	8	12	16	20	24
5	5	10	15	20	25	30
6	6	12	18	24	30	36

Dice 2

b) i) $\frac{3}{36} = \frac{1}{12}$

ii) $\frac{3}{36} = \frac{1}{12}$

iii) 0

8. a) $\frac{15}{78}$

b) $\frac{13}{78}$

c) $\frac{12}{78} = \frac{2}{13}$

ACKNOWLEDGEMENTS

The author and publisher are grateful to the copyright holders for permission to use quoted materials and images.

Every effort has been made to trace copyright holders and obtain their permission for the use of copyright material. The authors and publishers will gladly receive information enabling them to rectify any error or omission in subsequent editions. All facts are correct at time of going to press.

Letts and Lonsdale
4 Grosvenor Place
London SW1X 7DL

Orders: 015395 64910
Enquiries: 015395 65921
Email: enquiries@lettsandlonsdale.co.uk
Website: www.lettsandlonsdale.com

ISBN: 978-1906 -415-914

01/200309

Published by Letts and Lonsdale

© 2009 Letts and Lonsdale.

British Library Cataloguing in Publication Data.

A CIP record of this book is available from the British Library.

Book concept and development: Helen Jacobs
Commissioning Editor: Rebecca Skinner
Authors: Fiona Mapp
Project Editor: Emma Rae
Cover Design: Angela English
Inside Concept Design: Helen Jacobs and Sarah Duxbury
Text Design and Layout: Little Red Dog Design
Artwork: Letts and Lonsdale

Printed in Italy

Letts and Lonsdale make every effort to ensure that all paper used in our books is made from wood pulp obtained from well-managed forests, controlled sources and recycled wood or fibre.

8 The equation $x^3 + 2x = 7$ has a solution between 1 and 2. Use a method of trial and improvement to find the solution. Give your answer correct to one decimal place.

9 The equation $x^2 + 4x = 2$ has a solution between 0 and 1. Use a method of trial and improvement to find this solution. Give your answer correct to one decimal place.

10 Put the correct sign between these pairs of numbers:

a) 6 ⬚ 4

c) -5 ⬚ 4

e) -2 ⬚ -7

b) 8 ⬚ 7

d) 1.6 ⬚ 2.8

f) -3 ⬚ -6

11 Represent the following inequalities on the number lines.

a) $x < 7$

c) $x \leq -3$

b) $x \geq 3$

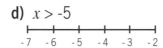

d) $x > -5$

Activity Create a spreadsheet to find the solution of Q9, $x^2 + 4x = 2$, to two decimal places.

Graphs

1 The graph opposite is used to convert between centimetres (cm) and inches.

Use the graph to convert:

a) 3 inches into cm.

....

b) 5.5cm into inches.

....

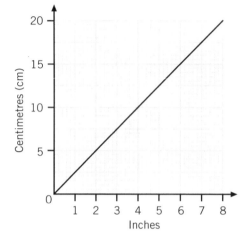

2 Alexa jogs in a straight line to the local shops and back. The graphs below describe the distance she jogs away from her house on four separate occasions. For each of the statements below, decide which graph describes it the best.

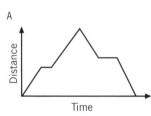
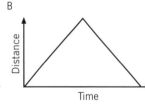
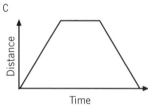
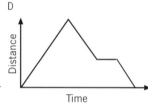

Graph

a) She runs at a constant speed to the shop and back without stopping.

☐

b) She runs at a constant speed to the shop and halfway back she has a rest.

☐

c) She runs at a constant speed to the shops, stops and buys a newspaper and then runs back at a constant speed.

☐

d) She runs to the shops and has a rest halfway, then runs back from the shop, again having a rest at halfway.

☐

1 Look at the coordinate grid and write down the equations of the following lines:

a) A ....

b) B ....

c) C ....

d) D ....

e) E ....

f) F ....

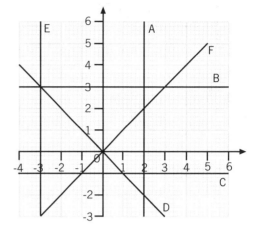

2 a) Complete this table of values for $y = x - 5$

x	-3	-1	0	1	3
y					

b) Plot the graph of $y = x - 5$ on the axes opposite.

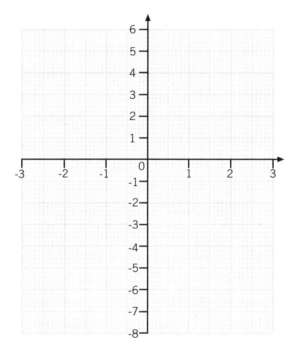

c) Complete the table of values for $y = x + 4$

x	-3	-1	0	1	3
y					

d) Plot the graph of $y = x + 4$ on the axes above.

e) What do you notice about the graphs of $y = x - 5$ and $y = x + 4$?

....

....

3 **a)** Complete the table of values for the function $x + y = 3$:

x	-1	0	1	3
y				

b) Plot the graph of $x + y = 3$

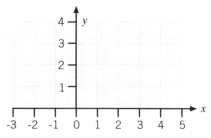

4 **a)** Complete the table of values for the function $y = 2x - 3$

x	-3	0	1	3
y				

b) Plot the graph of $y = 2x - 3$

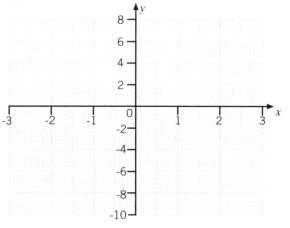

c) Complete the table of values for the function $y = 3x - 1$

x	-2	0	1	2
y				

d) Plot the graph of $y = 3x - 1$ on the axes above.

e) What are the coordinates of the intersection of $y = 2x - 3$ and $y = 3x - 1$?

_____

f) Plot the graph of $y = -3x$ on the axes above.

g) Which graph is steeper, $y = 2x - 3$ or $y = 3x - 1$?

_____

5 Match these equations with their graphs.

a) $y = 2x - 4$ ☐

b) $y = 2x + 4$ ☐

c) $y = 4x$ ☐

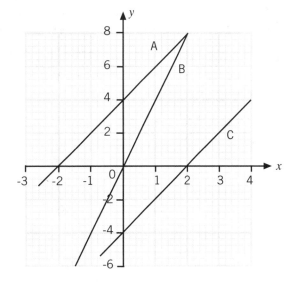

6 For each of the line segments, write down the coordinates of their midpoint.

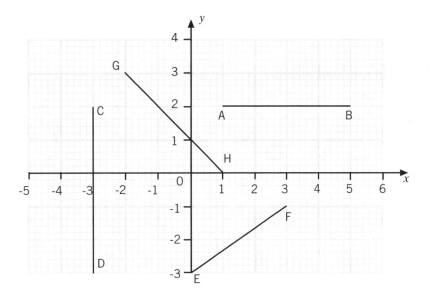

a) AB

....

b) CD

....

c) EF

....

d) GH

....

7 **a)** Complete the table of values for $y = x^2 - 4$

x	-3	-2	-1	0	1	2	3
y							

b) Plot the graph of $y = x^2 - 4$ on the axes. Join the points with a smooth curve.

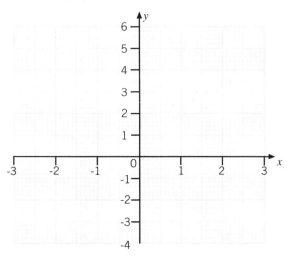

8 **a)** Complete the table of values for $y = 2x^2 - 3$

x	-2	-1	0	1	2
y					

b) Plot the graph of $y = 2x^2 - 3$ on the axes. Join the points with a smooth curve.

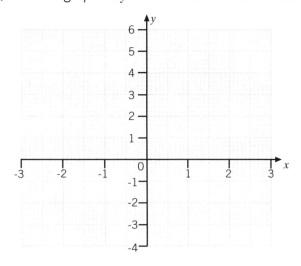

c) Write down the intercept of the graph $y = 2x^2 - 3$ on the y axis.

d) Where does the graph $y = 2x^2 - 3$ cut the x axis?

9 This distance–time graph shows two car journeys. Mr Davis is travelling from Mathstown to Summerton, whilst Mrs Hay is travelling from Summerton to Mathstown.

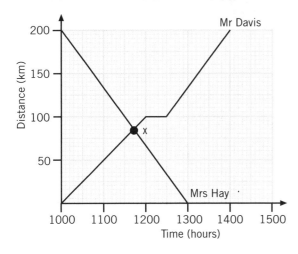

a) Who completes their journey in the fastest time?

_____

b) i) At what time did Mr Davis stop?

_____

ii) For how long did Mr Davis stop?

_____

c) Did Mr Davis travel faster in the first two hours of his journey or the last two hours of his journey?

_____

d) Describe Mrs Hay's journey.

_____

_____

e) What do you think point x represents?

_____

Shapes and Measure

1 Change...

   a) 7kg into lb   **c)** 7cm into inches

   b) 110lb into kg   **d)** 5 pints into litres

2 A plan has a scale of 1 : 30. If the width of a playground on the plan is 146m, what is the width of the real playground?

3 A map has a scale of 1 : 125 000. If the distance from a school to a church is 4.6cm, what is the real distance in km?

4 A dolls' house has a scale of 1 : 20. The width of a real house is 14m. What would the width of the dolls' house be?

1 The diagram shows a circle and its labels. Draw arrows to connect the labels with the correct parts of the circle.

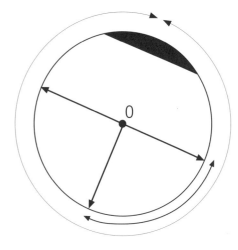

Arc

Diameter

Segment

Radius

Circumference

2 In the space below each solid, draw a sketch of its net.

a)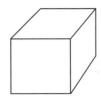

b)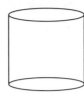

c)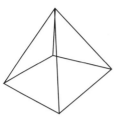

3 For this solid, in the space provided draw...

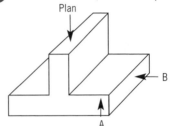

a) the plan

b) the view from A

c) the view from B

4 On this isometric paper draw a 3cm x 2cm x 1cm cuboid.

5 Using a compass and ruler:

a) Construct the bisector of this angle.

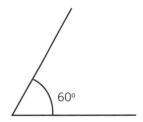

60°

b) Construct the bisector of the line segment AB.

A ————————————————— B

Angles

1. Work out the size of the missing angles. *NB Angles are not drawn to scale.*

a)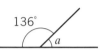

....

....

b)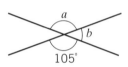

....

....

c)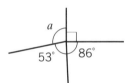

....

....

d)

....

....

e)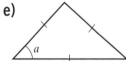

....

....

f)

....

....

g)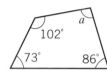

....

....

h)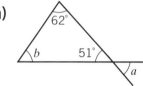

....

....

i)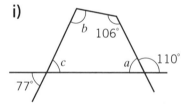

....

....

1. A regular polygon has 12 sides. What is the size of...

   a) the interior angle?

   ....

   b) the exterior angle?

   ....

2 Work out the size of angle *a* in this hexagon.

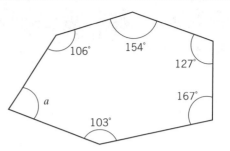

....

....

....

3 Work out the size of the missing angles in each of the following:

a)

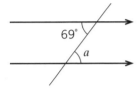

c)

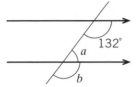

e)

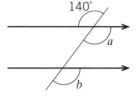

b)

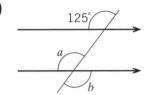

d)

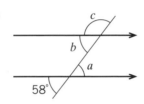

f)

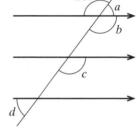

4 For each of the diagrams below find the bearing of:

i) A from B   **ii)** B from A

a)

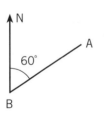

i) ....

ii) ....

c)

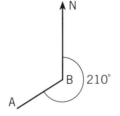

i) ....

ii) ....

e)

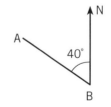

i) ....

ii) ....

b)

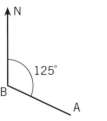

i) ....

ii) ....

d)

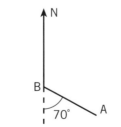

i) ....

ii) ....

f)

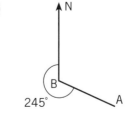

i) ....

ii) ....

Transformations

1. On the coordinate axes opposite, move shape A by...

   a) 3 to the right and 2 up. Label the shape B.

   b) 4 to the left and 5 up. Label the shape C.

   c) A translation of $\begin{pmatrix} -6 \\ -7 \end{pmatrix}$. Label the shape D.

   d) A translation of $\begin{pmatrix} 2 \\ -5 \end{pmatrix}$. Label the shape E.

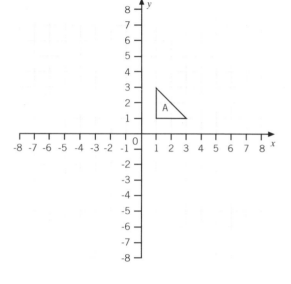

2. On the coordinate axes opposite, reflect shape P in...

   a) the x axis. Label the shape Q.

   b) the y axis. Label the shape R.

   c) the line $x = 4$. Label the shape T.

   d) the line $y = -2$. Label the shape U.

   e) the line $x = -2$. Label the shape V.

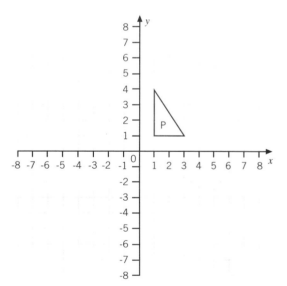

3 On the coordinate axes opposite, reflect shape W in...

   a) the line $y = x$. Label the shape X.

   b) the line $y = -x$. Label the shape Y.

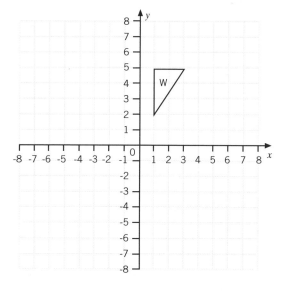

4 On the coordinate axes opposite rotate shape F...

   a) 90° clockwise about (0,0).
       Label the shape G.

   b) 90° anti-clockwise about (0,0).
       Label the shape H.

   c) 180° about (0,0).
       Label the shape I.

   d) 90° anti-clockwise about (-1,2).
       Label the shape J.

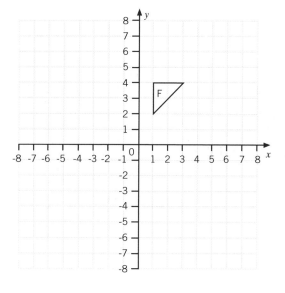

5 On the grid below, enlarge shape P by a scale factor of 3.

6 Decide whether the following statements are true or false.

a) A translation of $\begin{pmatrix} 5 \\ 4 \end{pmatrix}$ is 5 to the right and 4 upwards.

b) A translation of $\begin{pmatrix} 6 \\ -2 \end{pmatrix}$ is 6 to the right and 2 upwards.

c) A translation of $\begin{pmatrix} -10 \\ -2 \end{pmatrix}$ is 10 to the left and 2 downwards.

d) A translation of $\begin{pmatrix} -5 \\ -3 \end{pmatrix}$ is 5 to the right and 3 downwards.

e) A translation of $\begin{pmatrix} 4 \\ -4 \end{pmatrix}$ is 4 to the right and 4 downwards.

7 On the coordinate axes below enlarge shape A...

    a) by a scale factor of 2, centre (0,0). Label the shape B.

    b) by a scale factor of $\frac{1}{2}$, centre (0,0). Label the shape C.

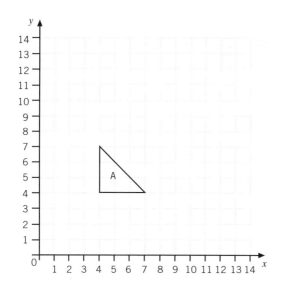

8 On the coordinate axes below...

    a) reflect shape D in the x axis. Label the shape E.

    b) reflect shape E in the y axis. Label the shape F.

    c) describe the single transformation that maps shape D onto shape F.

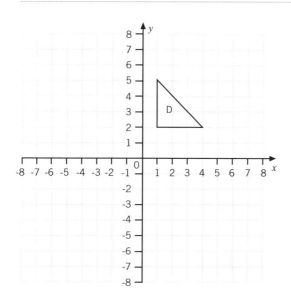

Perimeter, Area and Volume

1 For each of the rectangles below, find... *NB: Diagrams not drawn to scale.*

a)
6cm
4.2cm
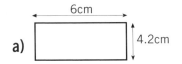

b)
13.5cm
10cm
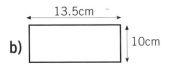

c)
19.3cm
9.4cm

i) area ....

ii) perimeter ....

i) area ....

ii) perimeter ....

i) area ....

ii) perimeter ....

2 The area and length of each rectangle is given. Work out the width of each rectangle.

NB: Diagrams not drawn to scale.

a)
7.2cm
Area = 28.8cm²
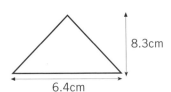

b)
10.7cm
Area = 74.9cm²
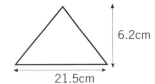

c)
36cm
Area = 504cm²
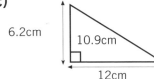

3 Find the area of each of these triangles. *NB: Diagrams not drawn to scale.*

a)
8.3cm
6.4cm

b)
6.2cm
21.5cm

c)
6.2cm
10.9cm
12cm

1 Find the area of each of these parallelograms. *NB: Diagrams not drawn to scale.*

a)

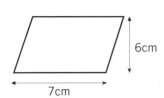

6cm

7cm

b)

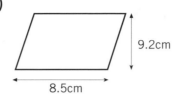

9.2cm

8.5cm

c)

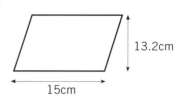

13.2cm

15cm

....

2 The area and length of each parallelogram is given.
Work out the height of the parallelogram. *NB: Diagrams not drawn to scale.*

a)

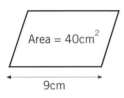

Area = 40cm^2

9cm

b)

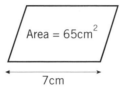

Area = 65cm^2

7cm

c)

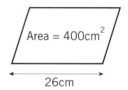

Area = 400cm^2

26cm

....

3 Work out the area of these trapeziums. *NB: Diagrams not drawn to scale.*

a)

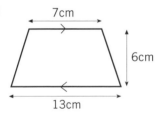

7cm

6cm

13cm

c)

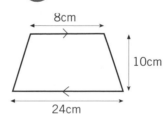

8cm

10cm

24cm

e)

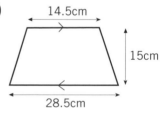

14.5cm

15cm

28.5cm

....

b)

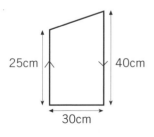

25cm 40cm

30cm

d)

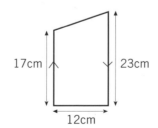

17cm 23cm

12cm

f)

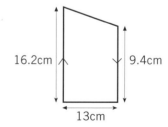

16.2cm 9.4cm

13cm

....

4 Find the area of each of these compound shapes. *NB: Diagrams not drawn to scale.*

a)

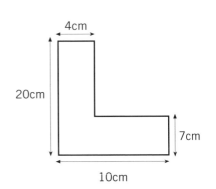

b)

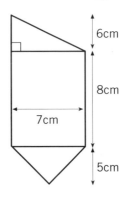

c)

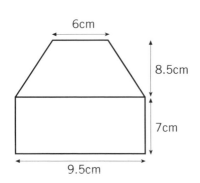

5 For each of the circles below find. *(Use π = 3.14. Give your answer to 2 decimal places.)*

a)

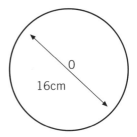

b)

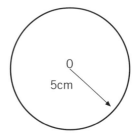

c)

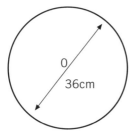

i) the circumference

i) the circumference

i) the circumference

ii) the area

ii) the area

ii) the area

6 Find the area of these semicircles. *(Use π = 3.14. Give your answer to 2 decimal places.)*

a)

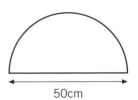

50cm

b)

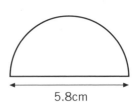

5.8cm

c)

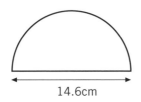

14.6cm

7 Find the perimeter of this semicircle. *(Use π = 3.14. Give your answer to 1 decimal place.)*

Perimeter = _____

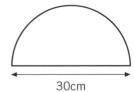

30cm

8 Find the area of the shaded region. *(Use π = 3.14. Give your answer to 2 decimal places.)*

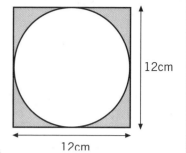

Area = _____

9 Find the volume and surface area of each of these cuboids.

a)

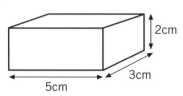

i) Volume

_____

ii) SA

_____

b)

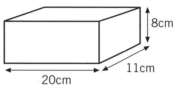

i) Volume

_____

ii) SA

_____

c)

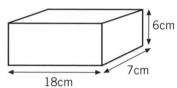

i) Volume

_____

ii) SA

_____

10 A metal crate measures 8m x 10m x 12m. Smaller crates of dimensions 3m x 4m x 5m are placed in the larger crate. How many smaller crates can fit in the large crate? *NB: Diagrams not drawn to scale.*

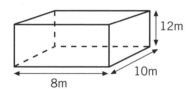

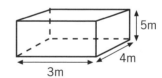

11 Find the volume of these solids.

a)

b)

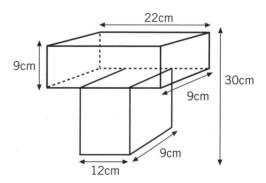

Volume = _____

Volume = _____

Handling Data

1 Simon asks this question in a questionnaire to find out how much television his classmates watch.

'How much time do you spend watching television?'

A bit ☐   About average ☐   A lot ☐   Lots ☐

Design a better question that Simon could ask.

2 The manager of a sports centre asks:

'How old are you?'

0–10 yrs ☐   10–20 yrs ☐   20–30 yrs ☐   Over 30 ☐

Explain what is wrong with this question.

3 Below are the heights (in cm) of 28 pupils in a year 8 class.

127 138 159 160 144 140 153 151 139 156

136 147 152 148 144 142 162 147 142

132 156 161 147 136 141 161 145 153

Fill in the frequency table below:

Height (h cm)	Tally	Frequency
$125 \leq h < 130$		
$130 \leq h < 135$		
$135 \leq h < 140$		
$140 \leq h < 145$		
$145 \leq h < 150$		
$150 \leq h < 155$		
$155 \leq h < 160$		
$160 \leq h < 165$		

3 (cont.)

b) Show this information in the frequency diagram below.

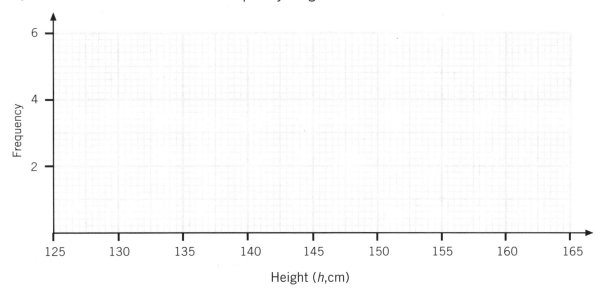

Height (*h*,cm)

4 Draw a pie chart of the data below.

Favourite Sport	Frequency
Football	8
Netball	4
Tennis	6
Rugby	6

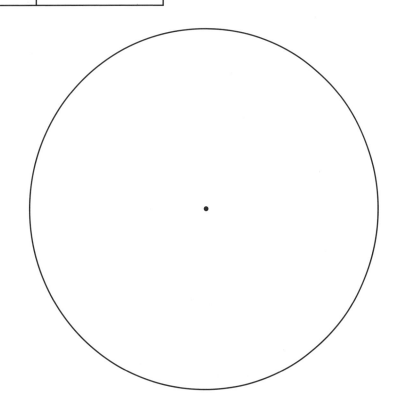

5 Here is a two-way table, which gives some information about the favourite colours of a group of students.

	Red	Blue	Green	Total
Boys	6	12		35
Girls		7	6	
Total	15			

a) Complete the table.

b) How many girls like red?

c) How many pupils were asked?

6 Here are the numbers of days off some teachers took through illness.

```
6  2  5  15  27  13  22
14  13  2  3  2  17  36
5  15  14  16  13  1
```

a) Draw a stem and leaf diagram to show this information.

b) What is the greatest number of days that a teacher took off through illness?

7 The table shows the marks scored by ten students in two Maths exams.

Exam 1	12	36	27	35	18	26	25	29	32	15
Exam 2	12	34	26	38	16	24	25	31	35	10

a) On the graph paper below, draw a scatter diagram to show the information in the table.

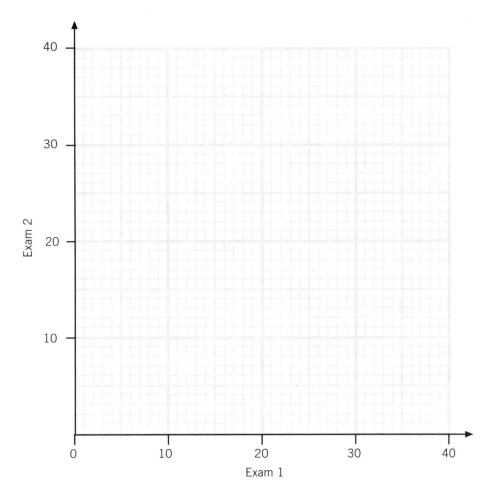

b) Draw a line of best fit on your diagram.

c) Using your line of best fit, estimate the mark a student got in Exam 2 if they got 29 in Exam 1.

Activity

For the above data use a spreadsheet to draw this scatter diagram. Compare it with your hand–drawn one.

Averages

1 For this set of data: 7, 4, 4, 3, 1, 6, 7, 4. Find the... 🖩

  a) mean ....   **c)** mode ....

  b) median ....   **d)** range ....

2 James and Lucy do three tests. Each test has a maximum score of 20. Here are their results:

	Mean Score	Range
James	15.7	1.7
Lucy	16.3	3.6

Who do you think did better in the tests? Give a reason for your answer.

....

....

Level 6

1 Find the mean, median, mode and range of the data in this table: 🖩

Number of Goals	0	1	2	3	4
Frequency	4	5	7	2	2

  a) Mean: .... goals   **c)** Mode: .... goals

  b) Median: .... goals   **d)** Range: .... goals

2 Find the mean, median, mode and range of the data in this table:

Age	12	13	14	15	16
Frequency	5	3	7	2	4

  a) Mean ....   **c)** Mode ....

  b) Median ....   **d)** Range ....

3 Use these stem and leaf diagrams to find:

a)

Stem	Leaf
1	0 2 2 5 7
2	2 2 2 2 3 6 8
3	1 9 9
4	0 5

   i)   Median ....

   ii) Mode ....

   iii) Range ....

Key: 2 | 6 = 26

b)

Stem	Leaf
7	0 3 7
8	5 5 5 5 9
9	2 6
10	7

   i)   Median ....

   ii) Mode ....

   iii) Range ....

Key: 8 | 5 = 85

c)

Stem	Leaf
22	7 8
23	5 6 7
24	3 4 4 4 4 7
25	1

   i)   Median ....

   ii) Mode ....

   iii) Range ....

Key: 23 | 5 = 235

d)

Stem	Leaf
5	2 7 7
6	8 8 8 8 9
7	2 3 3 4 5 7 9
8	6 6 7 9

   i)   Median ....

   ii) Mode ....

   iii) Range ....

Key: 6 | 8 = 6.8

Probability

Level 5

1 A box contains 3 red discs, 4 pink discs and a green disc. If you take a disc at random, what is the probability that you will choose...

a) a red disc? _____

c) a red or pink disc? _____

b) a green disc? _____

d) a purple disc? _____

2 The letters M, A, T, H, E, M, A, T, I, C, S are written on cards and placed in a bag. A card is taken at random. What is the probability that the card is...

a) the letter 'M'? _____

c) a vowel? _____

b) the letter 'T'? _____

d) a consonant? _____

Level 6

1 The probability that a buss is late is 0.35. What is the probability that the bus is on time?

_____

2 The probability of winning money on a 'Lucky Spin' game is 28%. What is the probability that you don't win any money on the game?

_____

3 The probability of passing a driving test on the second attempt is $\frac{6}{11}$. What is the probability of not passing on the second attempt?

_____

4 The probability that Nicola wins the 400m race is 0.83. Work out the probability that Nicola doesn't win the 400m race.

_____

5 Gill and Keith go to the drinks machine. They buy a drink each. The drinks machine has Cola, Apple and Orange. List all the possible combinations of drinks they could buy.

6 A spinner and a die are spun and thrown at the same time.
Their scores are added together.

a) Complete the sample space diagram below:

		\multicolumn{6}{c}{Die}					

<table>
<tr><td rowspan="5">Spinner</td><td>+</td><td>1</td><td>2</td><td>3</td><td>4</td><td>5</td><td>6</td></tr>
<tr><td>1</td><td></td><td></td><td></td><td></td><td></td><td></td></tr>
<tr><td>3</td><td></td><td>5</td><td></td><td></td><td></td><td></td></tr>
<tr><td>4</td><td></td><td></td><td></td><td></td><td></td><td>10</td></tr>
</table>

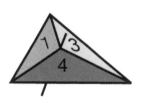

b) Find the probability of a score of...

    i) 5 ....

    ii) 7 ....

    iii) an even number ....

    iv) not a 6 ....

7 Two dice are thrown at the same time and their scores are multiplied.

a) Complete the sample space diagram to show the outcomes.

Dice 1

x	1	2	3	4	5	6
1						
2						
3						
4						
5						
6						

Dice 2

b) Find the probability of a score of:

i) 4 ....   ii) 12 ....   iii) 14 ....

8 The diagram shows a two–way table of sports done at a health club.

Sport	Male	Female	Total
Swimming	15	26	41
Squash	10	2	12
Running	12	13	25
Total	37	41	78

If a member of the health club is chosen at random, what is the probability that they...

a) are a male swimmer? ....

b) are a female runner? ....

c) play squash? ....